C000097813

Contents

Introduction

Developing the skills of sorting and matching

Sorting, comparing and matching objects helps young children to make sense of the world around them and to develop their powers of logic and reasoning. This book contains a range of practical activities designed to encourage that development. The early activities allow children time to explore their own ways of sorting objects, while at the same time encouraging them to think not just about *what* they are doing but also, and more importantly, *why* they are doing it. As their skills develop, they will be encouraged to apply different criteria to sorting activities and use different senses to help them match objects, thus ensuring a deep and lasting understanding of the processes involved. In the later activities, children learn to use a simple grid and up to three different criteria for sorting, and to match amounts and numbers up to ten.

Early Learning Goals

Although the activities in this book focus upon sorting and matching, they also cover a wide range of the Early Learning Goals for mathematical development. All of the activities encourage the use and development of a wide mathematical vocabulary and present opportunities to compare, sort and match everyday objects. Some of the activities cover things such as pattern ('Are they the same?', page 10), the awareness of simple number operations ('Count them and see', page 26) and the recognition and use of numbers up to 10 ('I can count', page 30), thus providing a good cross-section of mathematical experiences.

Baseline Assessment

Sorting by given criteria, and being able to explain sorting, form part of most formal Baseline Assessment schemes for mathematics, as does the use of mathematical language to describe size and position. Each activity in this book therefore includes a suggested assessment point which can be used either as part of each individual child's formal baseline assessment or as part of their record of achievement portfolio to aid future planning. This is in addition to the completed photocopiable activity sheet which accompanies each practical activity.

How to use this book

This book forms part of a series of books providing new ideas for developing early learning skills, and is designed to help all those working in a pre-school setting to provide their charges with the experiences necessary to be able to fulfil some of the Early Learning Goals by the age of five. Although it deals primarily with mathematics, it also provides opportunities to practise cutting, observation and pencil control – all of which form an essential foundation to learning in the early years.

The activities in this book make use of a range of resources which are readily available in most pre-school settings. They are complemented by a photocopiable sheet on the facing page that consolidates the learning that has taken place. This sheet can also be used as an assessment record or a record of achievement for individual children.

The activites are aimed at four-year-olds, but contain ideas to extend the activity for use with older or more able children, and ideas to support the younger or less able child. They are focused on a variety of areas found within most pre-school settings, such as the sand tray, the home corner and the play dough table.

The last page of this book contains a photocopiable Skills development chart which can be used as part of individual children's portfolios. It is designed to be completed by the adult and child working together, thus laying the foundations for self-evaluation and assessment which form an important part of the National Curriculum.

Progression

The activities in this book are presented in order of increasing difficulty, thus enabling it to be used systematically over a period of time to provide progression in the children's learning. The book begins by inviting the children to sort a range of everyday objects such as clothes, toy vehicles, fruit and vegetables, and moves on to include objects with specific attributes such as two- and four-holed buttons or coloured cutlery, before finally introducing geometric shapes and the use of sorting grids.

Home links

It is important to maintain positive links with the children's parents – either directly or through carers – so that you can work together to provide a secure foundation for learning. The final paragraph of each activity therefore contains suggestions for encouraging families to take an active part in their children's learning by encouraging them to follow up some of the activities that the children have undertaken in the group setting.

What shall I wear?

Learning objective
To sort everyday objects using a given criterion.

Group size
Up to four children.

What you need
A selection of winter and summer clothes; a snowy day picture; a picture of a summer day; photocopiable sheet; pencils; colouring materials.

Preparation
Make a copy of the photocopiable sheet for each child.

What to do
Look at the clothes and talk about them with the children. What do they feel like? What are they made of? Compare a T-shirt and a jumper. Which one do the children think would keep them warmer? Can they explain why? Repeat the comparisons with other items, such as a pair of trousers and a pair of shorts, or a cotton jacket and a thick coat.

Look at the seasonal pictures and suggest that the children might sort the clothes to go with the pictures. Encourage them to work together and talk about what they are doing. If they can't agree about where a particular item should go, put it to one side and discuss it with the whole group later.

Once all the items are sorted, compare the two piles. Are there any items that do not have a direct equivalent in the other pile? (For example, gloves, mittens and scarves.) And are there any items that belong in both piles? (For example, joggers and jeans.) Discuss the reasons for this. When you are sure that the children understand the differences between winter and summer clothing, give them each a copy of the photocopiable sheet.

Individual recording
Explain that the children in the pictures need some clothes to wear and invite the group to draw and colour them in. Talk to them as they work, reinforcing correct solutions with positive remarks to remind them of the task in hand. ('Well done, that coat has lovely long sleeves to keep her arms warm, hasn't it!') Look at the finished sheets with each child, encouraging them to tell you about their picture.

Support
Enlarge the sheet to A3 size and work with just one or two children, talking them through their drawings item by item.

Extension
Encourage the children to add plenty of detail to their drawings, such as patterns on scarves and zips or buttons on coats.

Assessment
Check whether the children can correctly identify items of clothing and can explain when they are worn.

Home links
Ask parents to talk with their children about the weather outside before deciding which clothes they should wear for a shopping trip or a walk to the park.

What shall I wear?

What's the difference?

Learning objective
To sort objects using own criteria.

Group size
One or two children at a time.

What you need
A collection of toy vehicles of all shapes, sizes and types; photocopiable sheet; scissors; glue.

Preparation
Make a copy of the photocopiable sheet for each child.

What to do
Look at the collection of toy vehicles together and talk about them. Encourage the children to name each vehicle and try to describe it. Talk about what makes the vehicle move, whether it travels across land, over the sea or through the air. Discuss whether it might be used for short or long journeys. Is it a quiet or noisy vehicle? What sound does it make? Does it travel quickly or slowly? What might it transport?

Suggest that the children sort the vehicles. Watch them as they work and encourage them to explain why they have put particular ones together. Once they have chosen a particular criterion for sorting, help them to use it consistently by reinforcing appropriate sorting with positive, encouraging remarks. ('Well done, now you've got three vehicles that travel on the sea! I wonder if you can find any more to go with them?') Let the children have several tries at sorting using different criteria. Once they are fully familiar with the activity, consolidate their learning by using the accompanying photocopiable sheet.

Individual recording
Give each child a copy of the photocopiable sheet and ask them if they can guess how to use it. Remind them of the vehicle-sorting activity that they have already done and invite them to cut out the vehicles and sort them into the two large spaces, however they like. When they are happy with their sorting, let them glue the pictures in place. Look at the finished sheets with each child, encouraging them to explain what they have done and jotting down their explanation on the back of the paper for future reference.

Support
Enlarge the sheet to A3 size and encourage the children to cut out all the vehicles before deciding how to sort them. Talk with them as they work to encourage them to keep to the same criterion throughout.

Extension
Encourage the children to colour the pictures on the photocopiable sheet neatly before cutting them out and to write a few explanatory words of their own.

Assessment
Note whether the children can choose and stick to their own criterion for sorting and whether they are able to verbalize what they have done.

Home links
Ask parents to talk to their children about the many different vehicles that they see when they are out and about and to notice the differences between them.

What's the difference?

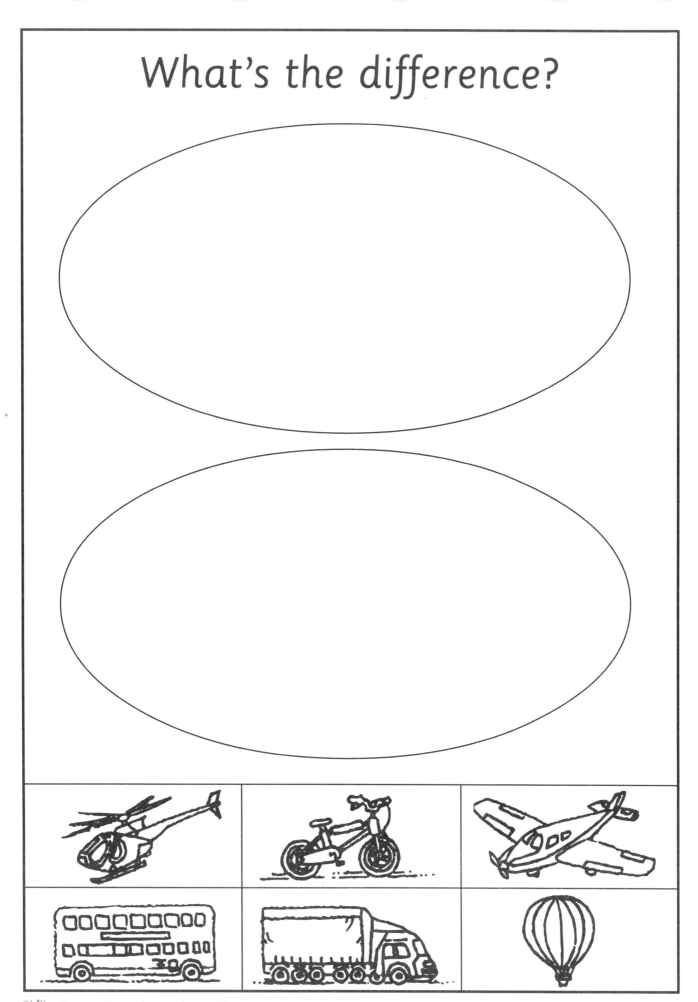

Fruit or vegetable?

Learning objective
To begin to know the difference between certain types of food.

Group size
Up to four children.

What you need
A selection of fruit and vegetables including those shown on page 9; a fruit bowl or basket; a vegetable rack; a sharp knife (for adult use only); a plate or cutting board; photocopiable sheet; scissors; glue; pencils; crayons.

Preparation
Make a copy of the photocopiable sheet for each child.

What to do
Let the children handle and talk about the fruit and vegetables. Make sure that they don't eat any of the produce in case of allergies. What do they feel like? What do they smell like? What are their names? Explain that some of these foods are called fruit and some are called vegetables. Cut an apple in half. What is inside

it? Cut a potato in half. Are there any seeds inside it? Explain that most fruits have seeds inside them and most vegetables do not. Invite a child to choose another item. Do they think it will have seeds inside? Cut it open and see. Is it a fruit or a vegetable? If it is a fruit, place it in the bowl or basket. If it is a vegetable, put it in the rack. Continue the activity until everyone has had at least one turn to choose an item. Then give each child a copy of the photocopiable sheet. Discuss the foods shown at the bottom of the page.

Individual recording
Invite the children to cut out the foods and lay the fruit on the basket and place the vegetables in a separate pile on the table. Check each child's work and praise them for correctly sorted items with reinforcing comments such as, 'Well done, that's right! Apples, grapes and oranges are all fruits so you can glue them into your basket now.'.

Support
Work with just two children and discuss each item as it is cut out, letting the child paste it into position straight away rather than waiting until all the items are cut out.

Extension
Before they cut out the pictures of food, encourage the children to colour them in as realistically as possible, using the real foods as a guide. Suggest that they draw a rack on the reverse of the sheet and glue on the vegetables.

Assessment
Check whether the children can correctly classify the foods and use the words 'fruit' and 'vegetable' without prompting.

Home links
Ask parents to help their children distinguish fruits from vegetables when they are out shopping together.

Fruit or vegetable?

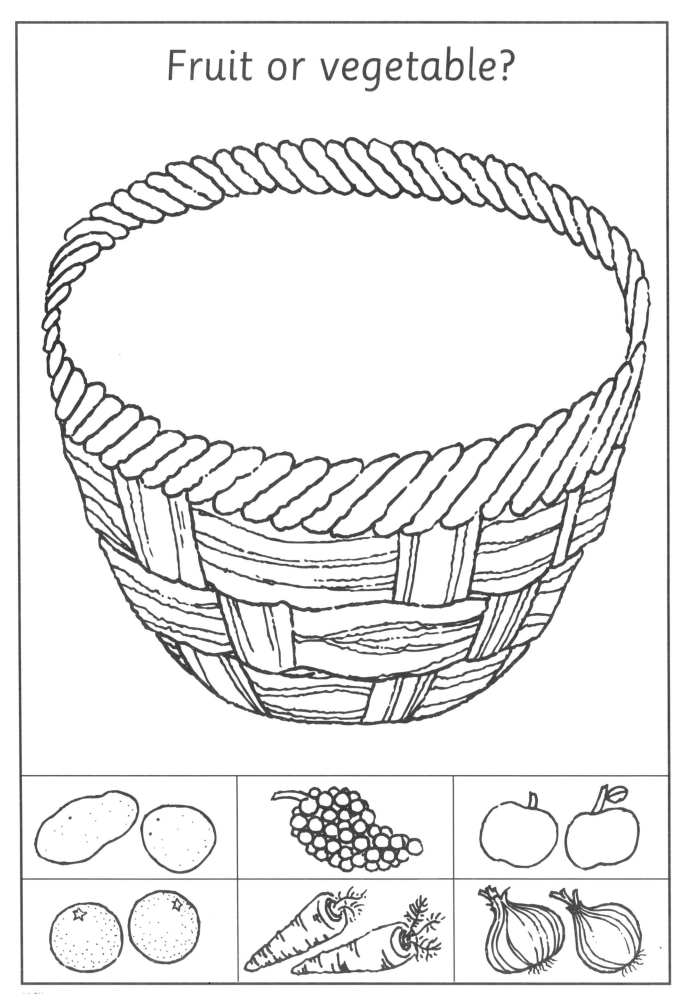

Are they the same?

Learning objective
To match identical objects.

Group size
Up to six children.

What you need
A selection of gloves and mittens in different sizes, colours and patterns; a box; photocopiable sheet; paints; thin paintbrushes.

Preparation
Make a copy of the photocopiable sheet for each child and also make one copy for yourself. Place one glove or mitten from each pair in a pile on the floor. Place the other gloves and mittens into a box.

What to do
Gather the group around the pile of gloves and mittens and invite the children to sort through them. What do they notice? Can they find any gloves that match each other in the pile? How can we tell when things match? (Because they

have the same pattern; they look the same as each other.) How many gloves do we need for our hands? Show the children the box of gloves. What do they notice about the pile and the box of gloves?

Sit the group in a circle and pass around the box, counting as it goes to each child. When it reaches every fifth child, let them take a glove from the box and try to find a matching one from the pile on the floor. If correct, the child may keep the pair. If incorrect, the gloves should be returned to the box or pile that they came from. Continue in this way until all the gloves have been correctly matched. Count the pairs of gloves that each child has to find a winner.

Individual recording
Show the children the photocopiable sheet and demonstrate how to make the mittens match by painting a pattern on one of them and folding the paper along the dotted line while the paint is still wet. (If the paint goes over the lines, cut out the mittens and mount them on a clean piece of paper.) When the mittens are dry, look at them together and talk about how the patterns match.

Support
Enlarge the sheet to A3 size and work with one or two children, restricting them to just two or three colours.

Extension
Suggest that the children try building up their patterns by folding the paper over after applying each different colour.

Assessment
Note whether the children can correctly match the pairs of gloves and whether they can name the colours in them.

Home links
Ask parents to let their children help to sort laundry by putting socks and gloves into pairs.

Are they the same?

What a muddle!

Learning objective
To sort items using two criteria.

Group size
One or two children.

What you need
A collection of cutlery in several different colours; plenty of tubs in which to store the cutlery; labels; scissors; coloured pencils; paper; photocopiable sheet.

Preparation
Label the tubs with pictures and words to show which items belong inside them, for example, red forks, green knives or blue spoons. Make a copy of the photocopiable sheet for each child.

What to do
Place all the cutlery together and invite the children to sort it in whatever way they like, encouraging them to explain what they are doing as they work. After a while, show the children the tubs. What do the labels mean? Challenge the children to re-sort the cutlery using the tubs. Check them together. Look at the label. Look at the cutlery inside the tub. Do they match? Are all the items the same? Are there some items that don't belong in the tubs? Let the children check each tub and decide whether it is correctly sorted.

Play some games by asking the children to close their eyes while you move some of the cutlery around. When they open their eyes, ask the children to say what is wrong and to put it right.

Individual recording
Give each child a copy of the photocopiable sheet and some coloured pencils. Tell them that you are going to see how clever they are at listening. Give them colouring instructions such as, 'Colour your knife and fork to match each other and your bowl and spoon to match each other' or 'Make all your cutlery match but make your plate a different colour.' Talk about the finished pictures, checking to see whether the children have fulfilled your criteria.

Support
Give instructions just one at a time. ('Colour your fork blue. Now make your knife green.')

Extension
Let the children issue colouring instructions to each other.

Assessment
On the back of the photocopiable sheet, jot down the instructions you gave, along with a few comments from the child about which items matched with which.

Home links
Ask parents to talk to their children about matching cutlery or crockery as they help with setting the table for a meal.

What a muddle!

Is this the one?

Learning objective
To match images of objects to the real items.

Group size
Up to three children at a time.

What you need
Several everyday objects (such as a chair, a wellington boot, a baseball cap, a pile of wooden bricks); close-up photographs of each of the objects taken from slightly unusual angles; photocopiable sheet; pencils.

Preparation
Place the everyday objects around the room in fairly inconspicuous places and make a copy of the photocopiable sheet for each child.

What to do
Spread out the photographs of the objects on a table-top and invite the children to look at them and talk about what they might depict. Now invite the children to try to find the actual objects somewhere in the room. Let them carry a photograph with them to help the identification process.

When the children think that they have found an object, encourage them to try to look at it from the same angle as the camera and to check small details for authenticity.

When the children are really sure about their find, let them leave the photograph with the object until all of them have been matched. Now make a tour of the objects together, checking that they are all accurately matched, before collecting up the photographs for use by another group later.

Individual recording
Give each child a pencil and a copy of the photocopiable sheet. Explain that it shows some more pictures of objects looked at from different angles. Challenge the children to find the matching pairs and join them with a connecting line. Look at the finished photocopiable sheets as a group and ask the children how they know that particular pictures go together. Encourage the children to hypothesize about the angle from which the objects may have been seen as well as their overall shape.

Support
Use photographs of familiar objects, taken from a not too unusual angle, and place the actual objects in fairly open view around the room.

Extension
Use black and white photographs – or photocopies of the originals – to make the activity more challenging and try to include some objects that are similar, such as two chairs of differing design.

Assessment
Note whether each child is able to notice similarities in shape and colour between the objects and their photographs.

Home links
Tell parents that you have been matching photographs and objects and ask them to help by looking at family photographs with their children and matching the images to the people and places shown in them.

Is this the one?

Odd one out

Learning objective
To identify objects that belong to a given set.

Group size
Up to four children.

What you need
A selection of coloured buttons of different shapes and sizes and with different numbers of holes; a small dish for each child; photocopiable sheet; colouring materials.

Preparation
Make a copy of the photocopiable sheet for each child. Display the selection of coloured buttons on a table.

What to do
Allow the group five or ten minutes to examine the buttons. Talk about their diverse colours and shapes and help the children to discover any similarities and differences between them. Are there any buttons that the children particularly like? Can they explain why they like them? Look at the number of holes in each button. Why are there no buttons with only one hole?

Now give each child a dish. For each child, start to make a set of buttons by putting in two or three that match. Challenge the children to find the remaining matching buttons to complete their set. Look at each set in turn with the whole group. Can anyone see any buttons that have been missed out of the set? How many buttons are in the set? Repeat this activity several times, giving the children different sets each time. Finally, let the children collect sets of their own and try to explain in what way their buttons match.

Individual recording
Give each child a copy of the photocopiable sheet and a selection of colouring materials. Encourage the children to look carefully at their sheet and to try to spot what is wrong with each set of buttons. Look at the 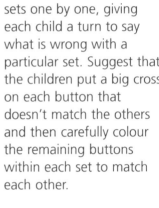 sets one by one, giving each child a turn to say what is wrong with a particular set. Suggest that the children put a big cross on each button that doesn't match the others and then carefully colour the remaining buttons within each set to match each other.

Support
Work with just one or two children at a time using a selection of very large buttons and restricting the number of shapes and colours.

Extension
Encourage the children to work together in pairs. Let them challenge each other to find different sets and to make direct comparisons between their sets to find which contains fewer or more buttons.

Assessment
Notice whether the children were able to accurately complete the sets of buttons that you started and whether they could make sets of their own.

Home links
Ask parents to help their children notice sets of buttons on a variety of articles of clothing. Ask them to encourage their children to talk about the features of the buttons and whether they match in size, colour and design.

Odd one out

Long or short?

Learning objective
To match objects by length.

Group size
Up to four children.

What you need
Plasticine or clay; blunt pencils; sturdy plastic cutlery; photocopiable sheet; clear plastic bag or laminating equipment; yellow crayons; red crayons.

Preparation
Make a copy of the photocopiable sheet for each child, plus one extra. Colour the extra one, and either place it in a sealable clear plastic bag for temporary protection or laminate it for long-term use.

What to do
Give the children some Plasticine and ask them each to make a straight snake. Suggest that they decorate their snakes by using the plastic cutlery or blunt pencils to make impressions in it.

Look at the finished snakes together and compare their lengths. Is one snake longer than all the others? Are any the same length as one another? Which is the shortest one?

Show them the laminated photocopiable sheet and challenge each child to make a snake that exactly matches one on the sheet. Let them lie their snakes on the sheet to check their lengths. Which of their snakes do they think is the longest and which is the shortest? How can they check? (By carefully straightening each one and lying them alongside each other with their heads aligned.) Lead them to notice what

happens to each snake's apparent length as it is straightened. Practise bending and straightening the snakes to ensure that the children understand that the length is conserved whatever happens to it.

Individual recording
Give each child a copy of the photocopiable sheet. Explain that you want them to colour the longest snake red and the shortest snake yellow. Can they remember which is which? Suggest that they use the laminated sheet and Plasticine snakes as before to check if they are unsure.

Support
Allow plenty of practice with straight snakes before introducing the idea of curves.

Extension
Suggest that they might use a piece of string to measure and compare the snakes on the sheet before colouring them in, rather than remaking the Plasticine models.

Assessment
Note whether the children understand the need to have a common baseline when comparing two or more objects. Do they also understand that the actual length remains the same even when the snake is curved?

Home links
Explain to parents that the children have been learning to compare lengths and ask them to help by encouraging their children to compare the lengths of shoes or socks belonging to different members of the family.

Long or short?

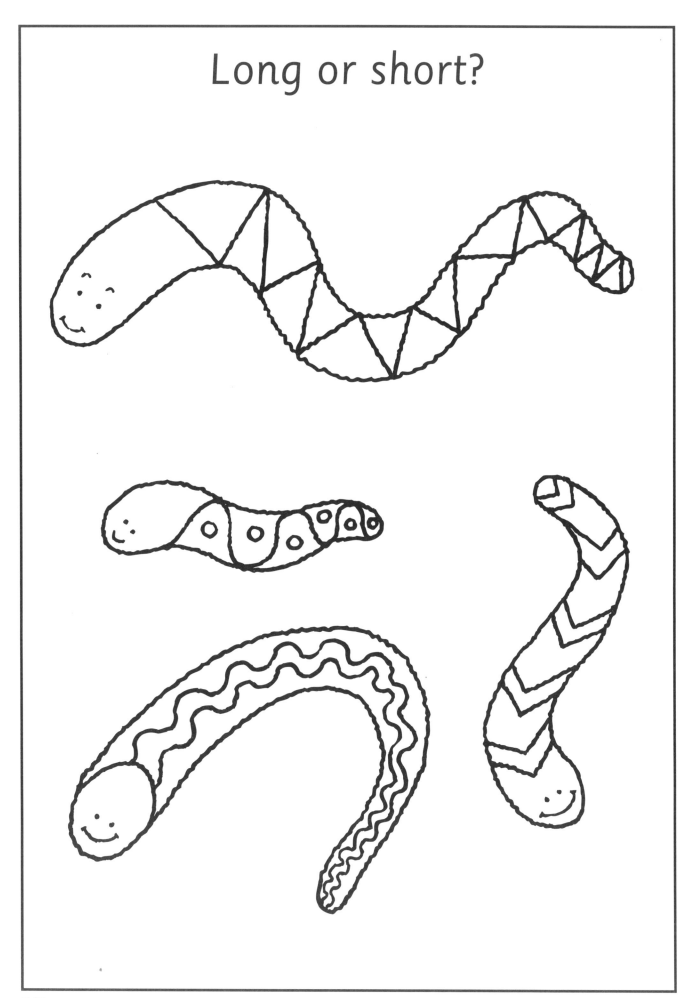

Can we unmix it?

Learning objective
To sort objects by size.

Group size
Two children.

What you need
A large bowl or deep tray containing a mixture of salt, uncooked pasta shapes (for example, penne) and rice; a few large spoons; colanders; sieves; containers of salt, pasta and rice, each labelled appropriately; strong glue; photocopiable sheet; thin card.

Preparation
Make a copy of the photocopiable sheet onto thin card for each child.

What to do
Show the containers and their contents to the children and explain that you have had an accident

– the containers have fallen over and spilled most of their contents and although you have managed to collect everything up in a bowl (show them the bowl), they are now all mixed up together. Can the children help you to sort them all out? Show them the colanders and sieves and tell them that you think these might be useful for sorting the items out, but you are not quite sure how to use them.

Stand back and let the children discover for themselves what to do. Talk to them as they work and ask questions such as: 'Why has the pasta stayed in the colander?' or 'Why isn't there any salt in the sieve?' Encourage them by expressing amazement at how well they are doing and how quickly they are collecting the pasta or rice.

When all the foodstuffs are back where they belong, discuss what the children have done and how they did it. Discuss the relative sizes of the foodstuffs and use comparative language (smaller than, bigger than).

Individual recording
Give each child a copy of the photocopiable sheet and ask them to record their sorting activity by gluing a little of each foodstuff into its relevant container.

Support
Enlarge the photocopiable sheet to A3 size. Talk to the children as they complete their sheets and help them to recall which item remained in which container, asking why this was so.

Extension
Give each child a copy of the photocopiable sheet and ask them how they think it should be completed. Encourage them to add a simple written explanation about their sorting activity – either scribed by an adult or written by themselves.

Assessment
Note whether the children understood why they were able to separate the foodstuffs with the sieves and whether they could explain this to someone else.

Home links
Ask parents to let their children practise comparing sizes by playing 'Size I Spy' with them. For example, 'I spy with my little eye something that is bigger than the kettle' or 'smaller than the cup'.

Can we unmix it?

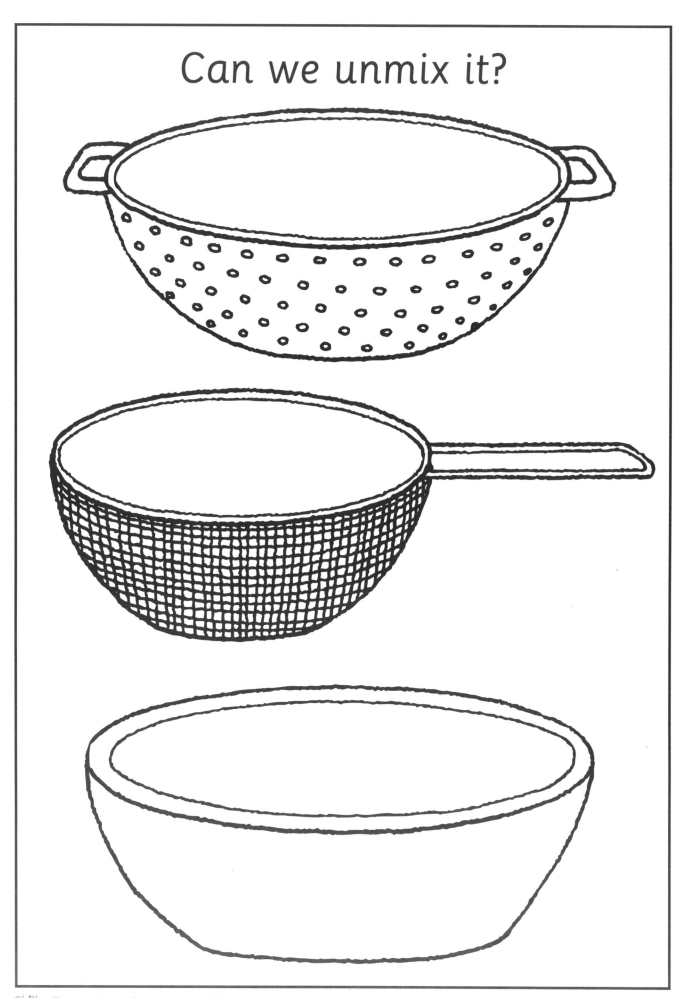

Which one is it?

Learning objective
To match sounds to the instruments that produce them.

Group size
Up to four children.

What you need
One of each instrument shown on the photocopiable sheet; scissors; large counters or buttons; a small screen to shield the instruments from view; photocopiable sheet.

Preparation
Enlarge the photocopiable sheet onto A3 card and cut along the lines to make a set of four lotto card strips. (If you plan to use them over a period of time, protect the cards by laminating them.)

What to do
Gather the group together and show them the instruments. Let them handle each one and listen to the sound it produces. Talk about the names of the instruments and explain that they are all percussion instruments. Listen again to the sound of each instrument in turn before putting them behind the screen.

Individual task
Give each child one of the lotto card strips and three counters. Explain that you are going to play an instrument behind the screen and that the children must listen carefully in order to hear which one it is. If they hear one of the

instruments shown on their card they must place a counter over it. Once anyone has covered all three instruments on their strip, the game is over. That child can then have a turn to play the instruments while the others listen.

Support
As each instrument is played, ask the group to tell you which it is. If they are right, congratulate them and show them the instrument so that they can match it with its picture on their cards. If they are wrong, ask them to listen carefully while you play it again.

Extension
Strike or shake each instrument only once. For really advanced listeners, play two instruments at a time for them to identify.

Assessment
Note the level of auditory discrimination displayed by each child and whether they are able to match each sound to the correct picture without needing to see the actual instrument again.

Home links
Encourage parents and carers to play 'I hear with my little ear' with their children at home, using familiar household sounds, such as the rattle of cutlery, the rustle of newspaper or the clinking of cups and mugs. Invite any musicians among them to come in to your setting and to play a short piece of music on their instrument to the group.

Which one is it?

Shape sorting

Learning objective
To sort objects using three criteria.

Group size
Two to four children.

What you need
A set of geometric shapes in three different sizes, shapes and colours; photocopiable sheet; scissors; crayons; felt-tipped pen; pencils; ruler; thin A4 card; A4 paper for each child.

Preparation
Copy the photocopiable sheet four times onto thin card. Cut each sheet along the lines and colour the appropriate cards blue, red and yellow. Shuffle the colour cards and place them face down in a pile. Do the same with the size and shape cards.

Using a felt-tipped pen, draw lines to divide an A4 piece of paper into four boxes. Make enough sheets for the children to have one each.

What to do
Spread out the geometric shapes and encourage the children to sort them using their own criteria. Talk to them as they work and encourage them to explain their methods of sorting. After several minutes, challenge the children to find specific things such as a big blue triangle or a small red square.

Individual task
Give each child a sheet of prepared A4 paper and show them each pile of criteria cards in turn. Ensure that they understand what each card means. Put the three piles of cards face down in the centre of the table and invite the children to take turns to take one card from the top of each pile. They then have to find a shape that fits all three criteria. If successful, players draw and colour the shape in a section of their paper before returning the cards to the bottom of their pile. The game continues until each child has drawn one shape in each section of their piece of paper.

Support
Use only two piles of criteria cards and use the found shape as a template to draw around.

Extension
Make a set of negative criteria cards to add to the pile by copying and colouring the photocopiable sheet, then putting a cross through each of the criteria. When a child takes three cards she might, for example, have to find a big shape that is *not* blue and *not* a triangle.

Assessment
Go through the completed sheet with each child and check whether they can describe the shapes they have drawn, using the three given criteria.

Home links
Ask parents to help their children by playing 'Describing I Spy', where they describe the object to be guessed using two or three different words, for example: 'I spy with my little eye, something that is big and green and furry'. (A toy dinosaur.)

Shape sorting

big	small
yellow	blue
red	

Count them and see

Learning objective
To match sets of up to five objects.

Group size
Up to four children.

What you need
Sets of five objects, large and small, for example buttons, teddies, pencils, cups, books; five small hoops; photocopiable sheet; pencils; crayons.

Preparation
Make a copy of the photocopiable sheet for each child.

What to do
Show the children the sets of objects and talk about the items. Make sure that all the children are familiar with them. Place two hoops on the table. Put three objects in one hoop and three in the other. Talk about the two sets with the children. Do they contain the same objects?

(No.) Do they contain the same number of objects? How can they tell? (By counting.) Give each child a hoop and keep one for your own use. Tell the children that you are going to make a set of objects in your hoop and that they must try to make a set with the same number of objects in their own hoop. Practise this several times, using different amounts up to a total of five and counting the sets together to make sure that they match.

Individual recording
Give each child a copy of the photocopiable sheet and a supply of pencils and crayons. Look at the sheet together and talk about the pairs of sets. Is there the right number of eggs to go in the eggcups? How can they tell? (By counting.) Discuss how to make the sets on the right match those on the left by crossing out or drawing in extra objects as appropriate. (Either the right- or the left-hand set may be altered. Leave the choice up to the child.) Look at each child's completed sheet with him and talk about what he has done, checking the sets together and how to rectify any mistakes.

Support
Use sets of up to only three items and allow extensive practical activity before embarking upon the photocopiable sheet.

Extension
Use amounts up to ten and introduce the words *more* and *less* as you work.

Assessment
Notice each child's ability to count accurately and to add or subtract objects to make matching amounts.

Home links
Ask parents to help their children to recognize and count small amounts of objects while out shopping – six eggs in a box, four apples on a tray, five bananas in a bunch.

Count them and see

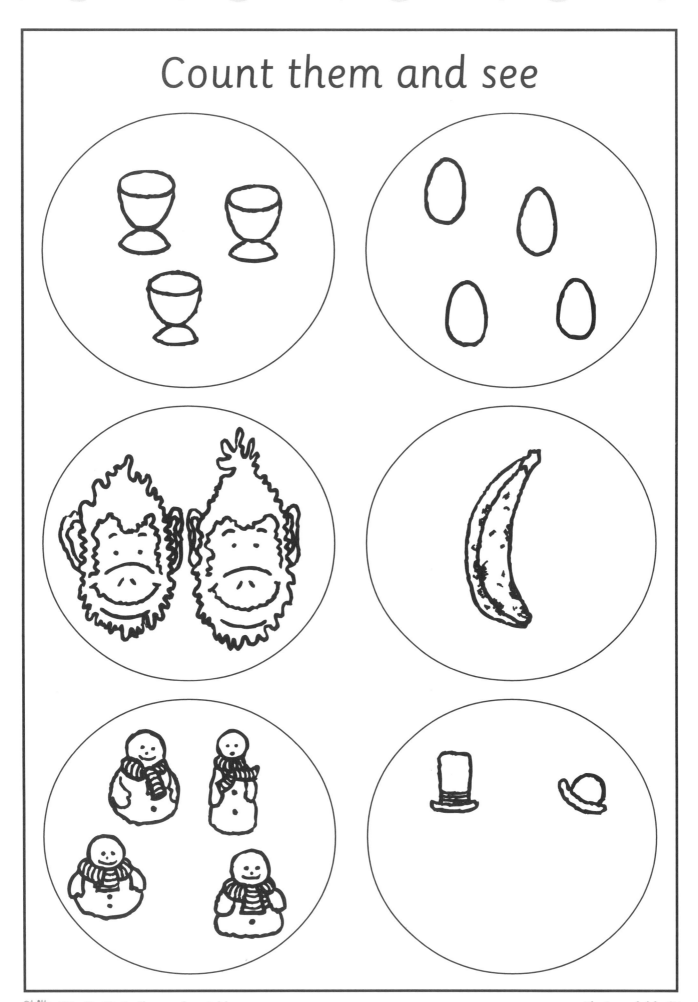

Where does it belong?

Learning objective
To sort objects onto a grid.

Group size
Up to four children.

What you need
A set of large and small circles, triangles and squares; photocopiable sheet.

Preparation
Make one copy of the photocopiable sheet for each child, enlarging it to A3 size.

What to do
Invite the children to explore the shapes and sort them freely. Talk to them as they work and notice any criteria that they use for sorting. After a while, stop the activity and draw the children's attention to any shapes that have been matched by both size and shape. Ask: 'I wonder why all these shapes have been put together?'. Praise any appropriate explanations and then suggest that perhaps the sorting would be neater if it were done on special grids.

Individual recording
Give each child a copy of the photocopiable sheet and ask them to think about how it might be used as a sorting sheet. Look at the sheet together and read the words at the top. Correctly position a small triangle and a large circle on the grid. Ask the children to explain why you have placed them there. If no answer is

forthcoming, point to the word 'large' at the top. Run your finger down the page to the circle and ask, 'What size is the circle?'.

Reinforce the correct answer with a positive comment such as, 'That's right! Well done. The circle is large and it's below the word "large". Now, why do you think I put the small triangle just there?'. (Point to the triangle.)

Once all the children understand that the shapes must be put next to similar ones and below the appropriate size words, invite them to sort the shapes onto their own grids.

Support
Cover the right-hand column so that the children work with just the large shapes. Then uncover it so that the small shapes can be sorted.

Extension
Introduce the words 'grid', 'column' and 'row' as you talk to the children about their work.

Assessment
Notice which children are able to use the grid with ease and which children need more practice at the activity.

Home links
Give each child a blank photocopiable sheet to take home, changing the words to 'Draw the correct shapes onto the grid'. Encourage parents to help their children to complete their 'homework' and bring the sheet back to discuss with the rest of the group.

Where does it belong?

	large	small
◯		
△		
☐		

I can count

Learning objective
To match sets of objects to their appropriate numbers.

Group size
Up to 12 children for the first part, but only two children at a time for the challenge.

What you need
Ten identical lidded boxes (shoe boxes are ideal); felt-tipped pen; a range of small objects in sets of one to ten; photocopiable sheet; glue; wool; scissors.

Preparation
Using the felt-tipped pen, write a figure 1 on the first box and its lid, 2 on the second and so on to 10. Make a copy of the photocopiable sheet for each child.

What to do
Show the children the boxes and let them watch and count aloud as you put the correct number of objects into each one and place its lid on top. Look at each lid in turn. What number does it have on it? How many objects do the children think there might be inside? Invite a child to count them to check.

Do this with each box to ensure that the children recognize the numbers and can count the objects accurately. Then take off the lids, muddle them up and replace them on the boxes at random. Challenge pairs of children to work together to sort them out. Watch them as they work and offer them encouragement and practical suggestions if they appear to be getting frustrated. When they have finished, check the boxes together to see if they are right.

Individual recording
Give each child a copy of the photocopiable sheet, wool, glue and scissors. Ask them to join the sets of objects to the correct numbers by sticking on lengths of wool.

Support
Use only five boxes and five sets of objects.

Extension
Empty the boxes and mix up their sets of objects as well as muddling their lids.

Assessment
Notice whether each child is able to use a logical strategy for sorting and matching the lids or whether they seem to be working randomly.

Home links
Ask parents to help their children notice numbers on the packaging of various items such as cakes, fish fingers, burgers and bread rolls when out shopping.

I can count

Name _____

Skills development chart

I can match amounts to numbers

I can sort objects onto a grid

I can match identical amounts

I can match sounds to their instruments

I can sort objects by size

I can match objects by length

I can identify objects that belong together in a set

I can sort using three criteria

I can sort objects using two criteria

I can match identical objects

I can sort objects by family

I can sort objects by myself

I can match objects to their photographs

I can sort objects following instructions